Samsung Galaxy Tab S6 / S6
Lite User Guide for Beginners

Complete Galaxy S6 Manual with
Tips, Tricks and Troubleshooting
common problems

Mary C. Hamilton

Dedicated

To

John

Mark

Luke

Natasha

I love you all...

Acknowledgment

I want to thank my colleagues at *TechVerse* for their support and contributions in making this work a success.

Table of Contents

INTRODUCTION

Grab a *Sammy Galaxy Tab S6*, and put it to work or play. You'll quickly see why it's rated as the best all-purpose, stylus-enabled, tablet. You'll also see why it perched at the top of the sales chart, as best-selling Android tablet on Amazon in 2020.

Tab S6 is good. But we aren't going to dress it in borrowed robes. It can't snatch the topmost position from Apple iPad Pro (12.9-inch). It didn't also displace Microsoft's Surface Pro X (13-inch) workhorse.

These two retain their top-end rankings, as best laptop replacement tablets. The devil is in their princely price tags of over $1,000 apiece. Their cost puts them above the average consumer, placing them in the bosom of the rich.

Galaxy Tab S6 offers near top-tier specs and functions, at half the cost of iPad Pro and Microsoft Surface Pro X. Reason Tab S6 may just be a better pick for you, or any cost-conscious person needing a business-class tablet.

You'll love many of Galaxy Tab S6 offerings, including:

- The brilliant display, hallmark of Samsung devices
- Fast performance due to a big RAM
- High quality sound by AKG, with Dolby Atmos tech
- Sizeable 7040mAh Li-Po battery that keeps going for as long as you wish to work, or play
- Thin and light body built, so you don't feel pain holding it up in use
- Its laptop replacement potential, and more.

Because your Tab S6 did well in the market, Samsung was moved to introduce a pocket-friendly Tab S6 Lite version in July, 2020, one year after the senior sibling became available for preorder. This midrange model should interest you, if you're the cost-conscious type, like me. At barely $300 apiece, Tab S6 lite also stands out as the best-selling budget tablet.

How to use this book

The manual you're reading offers simplified guides, like an easy-to-follow cook-book, to help you perform basic tasks in Galaxy Tab S6, or S6 Lite. You can pick up tips you never tried before, or refresh your mind on some tips you already use.

Further down the line, in **Chapter Two**, to be precise, we'll touch on the many ways in which Galaxy Tab S6 differs from the low-price Tab S6 Lite. Chapter three torchlights the exciting features of the S Pen, the functions that make stylus-enabled devices appealing to tech consumers. We hope you enjoy the reading, as you learn from this very readable compilation.

CHAPTER ONE

GETTING STARTED WITH GALAXY TAB S6 / S6 LITE

If you just unboxed the S6 tablet, this readable manual will launch you on sound footing, if you follow the simplified steps it offers.

It's tempting to turn on the device and start exploring its exciting features right away. I didn't wait to start jotting down my thoughts, or drawing sketches, with the S pen in the tab.

But, it's advisable to charge your device's battery first.

➤ Connect your Galaxy S6 Tab to wall charger

When you unbox any tech device, the first thing to do is connect it to a wall charger. Ok, we agree it's not based on tech wisdom. But there's a reason to do it.

Your device comes with a lithium polymer battery partially charged at the factory. You wouldn't commit a crime if you just grab it and hit the go button. At the same time, you'll be doing yourself some good if you connect it to some wall charger, and wait 1 hour before moving on with your setup.

Some manufactures recommend you leave phone battery to charge for 8 hours, or more, at the first instance, even if the battery fills up in 1 or 2 hours. It used to be important in the past, when Nickel battery technology stored memory of your starting battery level.

Nickel isn't in use again, and charging before you start to use isn't a tech issue. It's just a practical advice, to ensure you don't run out of power (and get negative first impression of your device), while trying to set it up or download the apps you'll need to operate it.

For your Galaxy Tab S6, in particular:

- Samsung recommends you charge the battery fully before turning on the tablet.

- To charge properly and maximize battery life, use charging devices and replacement battery approved by Samsung. Unapproved battery devices can cause damage. Besides, it'll void your warranty.

- Battery charging indicator may not show until 10 minutes or more after you connect to a wall charger. You need not worry when you plug the device to power source, but see no evidence the battery is charging.

- While charging, your tab and charging gears may heat up and stop filling up. Samsung says it's normal and not a reason to worry. Simply disconnect the device, wait for things to cool down, then go ahead and charge full.

If you want to use the factory charge to flag off your setup, you can do your wish, provided you find enough juice to take you through the setup process. Or you take up your power bank for a backup.

> ## Turn on your Samsung Tab S6

After you've filled up your battery with juice, you can turn on your device and begin the setup process.

To turn it on:

- Simply press and hold the Side key for a couple of seconds for Galaxy Tab S6 screen to come up

- To turn it off, press **Side key** and **Volume down** button at one time. in the alternative, pull down the Notification panel, touch **Power** icon, then tap the **Power off** red icon

- To Restart your device, navigate **Notification panel** > **Power** > **Restart**

You can access more information via **Settings** > **Advanced features** >**Side key** > **How to power off your phone**

Setup wizard can help you all the way.

Once you turn on your Tab S6 the first time, *Setup Wizard* will guide you to do the following:

- Choose your default language
- Connect to a Wi-Fi network
- Set up various accounts
- Choose location features, and more

➢ **How to choose a default language for your Tab S6**

1. Swipe up from Home screen to display all apps

2. Open the **Settings** page

3. Touch **General Management** and select **Language & Input**

4. Choose **Language**. Then tap **Add Language**

5. From the page that opens, choose your primary language from the list of options.

Most people reading this manual and understanding it, may choose English as the primary language in their Galaxy S6 tab.

It' should be noted that Galaxy tab S6, like other Google Android devices, supports nearly 50 languages. These include many variations of English language aside the American and British versions. Depending on where you live, you can select Canadian

English, Indian English, Australian English, Irish English, and more.

➢ How to change language in Samsung Galaxy Tab S6

But after choosing a language, you may want to change it to another one, for polyglots or those who speak more than one language. Well, the steps you follow to change a language are not different from the steps you followed to set it up in the first place.

1. Get to your apps by swiping up on the **Home screen**

2. Open the **Settings** page

3. Touch **General Management**. In the alternative, tap **My Device**

4. Then, touch **Language & Input**. Select Language.

In the language options provided, select the new one you want to use.

> ## Connect your Galaxy tab S6 to Wi-Fi

Connecting your tab to a Wi-Fi will help you gain full access to the online support you'll definitely need for your setup. You can also use cellular data offered by your SIM card issuers to access the internet.

To connect to an available Wi-Fi network,

1. Swipe up on empty spot in Home screen to display your apps tray

2. Open the **Settings** app

3. Tap **Connections** and choose **Wi-Fi**. Switch on Wi-Fi if it's not already on

4. From the list of search networks tap the one you want to use to access the internet.

If asked, enter the password to connect. And once you do, the network will be saved in your device to hasten your access to it when you come within its range.

➢ **Copy data from Android devices**

As soon as your Galaxy Tab S6 is up and running, the first task you'll face is how to move your personal data and files from an old device into the new one.

It's not a daunting task, anyway. It's even easier if you're copying from another Galaxy device. But no matter where you're copying from, there are a number of options to choose from.

- **Copy data wirelessly via Wi-Fi/Samsung Smart switch**. This remains the number one choice if you're moving files from one Samsung Galaxy device to another.

- **Upload files to Google Drive and restore them to the new tablet.**

This option becomes very convenient when transferring files between Android devices.

- **Use USB cable to and adapters to transfer data.**

You'll like to use this copying method if you're importing data from a Mac or Windows device to your Galaxy S6 tab.

- **Transfer data via third party apps.**

Third party apps like **Coolmuster Mobile Transfer** can help you copy files most of the time. **Xender** is also very good to use in sending files across devices of all types.

We'll quickly go through a couple of the many options.

> ### How to transfer data to your new Galaxy Tab S6 wirelessly via Samsung Smart switch

1. Get Smart Switch by doing any of these:
   - Download Smart Switch from Google Play Store, in both of your Galaxy devices
   - From **Settings**, touch **Accounts and backup** > **Smart Switch**

2. Place devices near each other, not more than 50 cm (1.8 ft) apart

3. Then, open the app in both devices and touch the **Connect button** in one of them, to initiate a hook-up

4. Once connected, you'll see dada
   and file types. Choose the ones you
   want to copy and tap **Transfer**

   On your new Galaxy Tab S6
   (destination device), you'll be
   prompted to accept the incoming
   files.

5. Tap **OK** to continue

6. When you're done copying
   everything you want from your old
   device, tap **Done** to exit the action.

> ## How to copy data via Wi-Fi Direct

You can also copy data wirelessly,
using the Wi-Fi Direct feature, provided

your old and new devices are connected to the same Wi-Fi network.

1. From **Settings**, tap the Wi-Fi Connections icon (like butterfly wing)

2. Choose **Wi-Fi** and tap the toggle to turn it on

3. Select **Wi-Fi Direct**

4. Tap a device from the options, and follow onscreen guide to connect.

Then choose the files you want to copy from your old device and tap Wi-Fi Direct to share them to your Galaxy Tab S6.

➤ Transfer data from old device to your Galaxy S6 tab via Google Drive

First ensure everything you'll like to copy is backed up in Google Drive. All kinds of digital files can be securely stored in the cloud Drive. They could be music, videos, photos, and more. Once there, you can access them across devices, anytime, and from any location. Providing, of course, there's an internet connection.

Getting your data from Google Drive cloud storage to your new Galaxy Tab S6 is easy, for the fact you're operating within the same Google tech ecosystem.

It's in fact possible for all your valuable files in old Android device to sync in your new tablet automatically, after you sign in to it with the same Google account you used to store files in the old device.

So, if your Samsung Galaxy tab didn't come preloaded with Google Drive, this app should be one of the first you install from Google Play Store. Also get a copy of Google Drive Software in your desktop computer, to ensure files can sync smoothly between your new tab and your PC. Both are free to download.

To actually sync the two devices,

1. Sign in to your old and new devices with the same Google account

2. On your computer, open **Google Drive** app

3. Also open Google Drive app on your S6 Tab. Accept terms and privacy terms, if prompted

4. Use the **Share** icon on the apps to sync data in both devices.

That's it. When you're done syncing, every data you've got in Google Drive will be available also in your new device.

CHAPTER TWO

GALAXY TAB S6 / S6 LITE: HOW THEY DIFFER

The Galaxy Tab S6 twins look alike differ only in name, physical appearance and how you operate their shared features. They play in different leagues when it comes to specs, performance, pricing, and more. While Tab S6 plays in the top-tier, the less-endowed Tab S6 Lite is midrange, targeted at cost-conscious consumers, outside the US.

➤ **Operating System**

Your Tab S6 runs Android 9.0 Pie, upgradeable to Android 10.0, One UI 2.5, while Tab S6 Lite operates on Android 10 and Samsung branded user interface, One UI 2.0

➢ Processor

Galaxy Tab S6's CPU is loaded with powerful Qualcomm Snapdragon 855, in Octa-core architecture.

The junior sibling, Tab S6 Lite, relies on Samsung's trademark Exynos 9611 (10nm) chipset.

➢ GPU

Adreno 640 for Tab S6, and Mali-G72 MP3 for S6 Lite

➢ RAM

Huge 6 GB / 8 GB options put Tab S6 ahead in the performance race, compared with the 4 GB access memory for Tab S6 Lite.

> ➢ **Storage**

Tab S6 offers 2 internal storage sizes of 128 GB or 256 GB. Tab S6 Lite offers single option of 64 GB.

> ➢ **Expandable Memory**

The same for both devices: MicroSD slot 512 GB & up to 1 TB (not sold with device). Single SIM (nano).

> ➢ **Display**

Premium Tab S6 parades a brilliant 10.5 inches of display (measured from top right corner down to bottom left cubicle). Its Samsung's trademark

Super AMOLED panels, known for vibrancy; FHD (2560 x 1600) resolution, at 287 pixels per inch. Features high dynamic range (HDR10+) color reproduction.

Tab S6 lite isn't as bright, or as accurate in color rendition, with 10.4 TFT LCD (thin-film-transistor liquid crystal display) capacitive touchscreen, 16M colors. Resolution is lower, at 2000 by 1200 megapixels at 224 pixels per inch (ppi).

Which is not to say the Tab S6 Lite display is deficient. It's good enough for the price. But not comparable to the vibrant smoothness you find in the high-end Tab S6 display.

➤ Camera

Talking about camera, Tab S6 still maintains a comfortable lead over the Tab S6 Lite. It's got dual rear shooters: 13MP ultra-wide f/2.2 sensor, and 5MP wide f/2.0 shooter. In the front, you find an 8MP f/2.0 selfie snapper.

In the Tab S6 Lite, Samsung also compromised on camera arrangement to keep production cost low, so users can pay less to own a good Android stylus tablet. You have an 8-megapixel sole snapper at the rear, and a 5MP selfie.

➤ Battery

Both Galaxy Tab 6 models are powered by Lithium polymer battery, maximum rated capacity 7040mAh, non-detachable. Nonetheless, your Tab S6 internal power source is capable of enduring 15 hours of normal use on a single charge.

> ➢ **Body build**

Glass front, aluminum frame, aluminum back

> ➢ **Dimensions**

Height, Width and Depth, the difference in dimensions between Tab S6 siblings isn't much at 9.63 x 6.28 x 0.22 inches (244.5 x 159.5 x 5.7 mm) for the elder. And 9.63 x 6.07 x 0.28 inches (244.5 by 154.3 by 7 mm) for the junior Tab S6 Lite model.

➢ **Weight**

Given its relative greater thickness, it isn't surprising that Tab S6 Lite weighs slightly heavier than top-of-the-market Tab S6.

Respectively, the score is 0.926 lb (420 grams) for one, and 1.03 lb (467 grams) for the winner.

However, both are light enough to hold up, for work or play, over a reasonable time, without much discomfort.

➢ **Connectivity**

Wi-Fi 802.11; Bluetooth v5.0 and USB type-C.

➢ **Color**

3 color options for each model: *Mountain Gray, Cloud Blue* and *Rose Blush* for the top-flier.

Chiffon Pink, Angora Blue and *Oxford Gray* for the midrange.

> ➢ **Price**

Galaxy Tab S6 (6 GB / 128 GB) can be yours for $629 on Amazon, or 600 Euro in the Europe.

Tab S6 Lite, costs $343.19 in the US but $429.99 for international buyers. It goes for 380 Euro if you're in Europe.

CHAPTER THREE

HOW TO USE S PEN IN TAB S6 / S6 LITE

The S Pen function is one of the key attractions of Samsung Galaxy Tabs and Galaxy Note series. A stylus in any device gives you the power to do more. You can quickly jot down your thoughts and observations as they come, so they don't escape your mind. And you can occupy yourself with creative drawing, or doodling.

First, you need to setup the S Pen before you can use it. Plus, you'll endeavor to use only the pen that's made for your own tablet model, or you risk damaging your capacitive screen.

Getting Started with Air Command menu

The Air command menu displays all the exciting things you can do with the S Pen in your Tab S6, including Smart select, Live (animated) message, Augmented Reality (AR) Doodle, and more.

To access Air command menu,

- Hover your S Pen over Tab S6 screen
- Touch the floating Air command icon that appears

Then choose what you want to do with your S Pen. Among other things, you can choose to:

- Create notes
- Use Screen write
- Smart select
- Screen write
- Live messages
- Translate foreign languages
- Use Direct pen input, and lots more

How to create quick notes in Samsung Notes

A stylus-enabled device allows you to quickly put your ideas down in writing before they escape your mind. After all, we live in an age of distractions and poor concentration. To create a quick note,

1. Tap the **Air command** icon with the S Pen to open the menu

2. Touch **Create memo**. A Samsung Notes window will pop up for you to write, or draw

3. When you're done jotting your thoughts, tap **Back** to save what you've written to the **Notes** app, the default destination of all notes.

To view everything you've saved in Samsung Notes app, tap **View all notes** in the Air command menu.

How to use Direct pen input

The Direct pen input mode lets you write a text in long hand, instead of typing it on a keyboard. The feature is activated by default, but can be turned **off and on**, in your S Pen settings. Try it right away by doing the following:

1. Open any app where you can type with on-screen keyboard
2. Hover over the text area with the S Pen
3. Select Handwriting icon in the options.

Your on-screen keyboard will turn to plain board where you can write a text with old-time long hand, something that's almost fallen into disuse since the spread of keyboard equipment.

Using Smart Select to screenshot in Galaxy Tab S6

Capturing things on the screen is what we do often, either to share with friends or store for future reference. Sometimes, what we really need is just a portion, not the entire screen. Smart Select and your S Pen allow you to screenshot only the precise part of the screen that contains what you want.

1. Tap the **Air Command** icon with your S Pen

2. In the menu that opens, touch **Smart Select**

3. Choose the type of capture you
   want
   - Rectangle
   - Lasso
   - Oval
   - GIF
   - Pin to screen
4. Take the screenshot of a portion of
   the screen with your S Pen
5. Tap **Save**

When the image is captured, you've got
six options of what to do with it.

- **Extract text**: This option will make
  words from your screenshot appear
  at the lower part of your screen. You
  can then tap **Copy** to place in your

clipboard, touch **Share** to send it to Nearby devices, or to other apps.

- **Auto select**: Enables Smart select to bring out the main subject of the screenshot.

- **Draw**: You can choose this option if you want to edit, or draw directly in the screenshot. After, you can save it to Gallery.

- **Pin to screen**: That's what you choose if you want the screenshot to appear on your screen so you can save it, move it around, or close it.

- **Share**: This option lets you share the screenshot the way you'll share any other image or file, through email or text, and more.

- **Save**: This is what we do most often with screenshots. Save and send it to the Gallery app.

With the S Pen, taking a screenshot in your Galaxy Tab S6 offers a whole lot of possibilities, as you can see from the bullet points above.

How to use the Screen write feature

This S Pen function lets you take a screenshot and highlight relevant parts of a document, or email, that you're forwarding to a friend or colleague. You'll help the receiver to focus on what's really important, instead of wasting time to pore over triviality.

1. Open **Air Command** menu, by tapping the icon (black circle with a white slash inside) with your S Pen

2. Touch **Screen write**. The device will screenshot your current page

3. You can crop, write, and draw directly on the screenshot.

Afterward, you can share it with your friends or colleagues, and save it in your Gallery app.

Send a Live message with S Pen

Text messages often look bland and boring. Good a thing, they're also short by design. But you can enliven up your messages by using this S Pen feature, which lets you put life into your writing, and animate your drawing.

1. Tap the **Air Command** icon (black circle with white slash insert) with S Pen

2. Select **Live message**

3. Touch a background from the options, then tap **Start writing.** Note: You can pick your background from:

   - **Gallery**: Choose existing photo you saved here

   - **Google Photos**: Take a background from the ones you stored here

   - **Camera**: Draw or write on a new picture or video and tap Capture to make a photo, or tap and hold to record a short video to use as background

- **Color**: Draw or write on a background, select the color you want. Then tap **Start writing**

4. After choosing a background, font color, style, and whether to save the **Live message** as MP4 or GIF, proceed to write a message or draw an image. This is instantly recorded and animated

5. Tap **Done** to save it.

Now, you can touch the Share button to send the **Live message** to friends or family members via text or other options.

How to translate text in Tab S6 using the S Pen

Imagine searching something important, only to have been suggested webpages in a language you cannot understand. If this language is among the ones supported, you can read the webpages, thanks to your S Pen translation capacity.

1. Using your S Pen, touch the **Air Command** icon to open its menu

2. Tap **Translate**

3. Touch the source language, then touch the target one. Hover over each word to translate it to your target language

4. Tap the Sound icon (like loudspeaker) to hear word pronounced in the source language).

It's best to translate whole sentences instead of words. Tap **Phrase translate** icon for this purpose.

When you're done using this feature, tap Close button **X** to quit.

Using the Screen off memo

Good to know you don't always have to unlock your Tab S6, or turn it on, to be able to write a note or draw an image in device. The screen off memo option has to be enabled in your S Pen configuration before you can use it. To create a Screen off memo,

1. Detach the stylus when the Tab is turned off, and write or draw on the screen

2. Tap an option to tweak your memo or image
   - Tap **Color** option to change color
   - Tap **Pen** tools to use them
   - Tap **Eraser** icon to erase words or all you've written

When you finish your memo or drawing, tap **Back** > **Save** to save it to **Samsung Notes**.

Apps that you can use with Air Command

Your Air command goes with a number of default apps and features like

Camera, Augmented Reality (AR), Calendar, Chrome, Contacts, Google Drive, and more. But you can add more apps.

1. Touch **Air command** icon with S Pen to display its menu

2. Look at the lower part of your screen and touch **Add Shortcuts**

3. Select any app you want to add, and it'll appear in Air command menu

You can remove the app you added at any time you change your mind about it. Simply tap the **Delete** button (red) next to the app you want to remove.

_____

Adjust S Pen settings in your Tab S6

You can customize many features of the S Pen, thus choosing how you want them to work in your device.

1. Swipe up from the center of your Home screen to display all apps

2. Tap **Settings**, select **Advanced features**

3. Touch **S Pen** to begin adjusting its settings

- **Air actions**: Choose how remote control works while you're using a compatible app

- **Unlock with S Pen remote**: Set S P to unlock your device. You must set a secure screen lock to use this feature.

- **Screen off memo**: Enable this feature so you'll be able to create notes when your Tab S6 screen is turned off.

- **Pointer:** Turn it on to make the pointer appear on your device's screen when the tip of S Pen is near the screen, displaying available options.

- **Air command**: organize your Air Command menu with S Pen capacities, and make it show a floating action that you can move around on the screen.

- **S Pen Removal**: Choose what happens when S Pen is detached from the Tab. You can choose to

Open Air command, **Create note**, or **Do nothing.**

- **General**: Tap here to get more information about the features of S Pen and how to use them.

Savor S Pen Air view features

When you've enabled the Pointer, and when the pointer shows a solid color, you enjoy the Air view features, which basically allow you to preview content or information about items on a screen, without opening them. You can do any of these:

- Hover over an email message to preview the content before opening it

- Check out the content of a photo album, or enlarge a photo just by pointing S Pen over them.

- Preview a video, even go to specific scenes in the footage, by tracing the timeline with S Pen

- View the name or information about an icon, again, by simply hovering over the item with your stylus.

That's the much we can take on the stylus. We've devoted much time to it because it's viewed as an outstanding feature of any device that offers note-taking capability. We'll now talk about how you navigate Galaxy Tab S6.

CHAPTER FOUR

NAVIGATING YOUR TAB S6 / S6 LITE

In navigating or exploring your Galaxy Tab S6 twins, it's good to bear in mind that you don't need excessive force, or press hard to get things done on your screen. The capacitive touchscreen responds well to any light touch with the palm of any finger. In fact, a hard hit can damage the tempered glass surface of your screen, and void your warranty.

How to personalize your Tab S6 Home screen

The Home screen is where you place your favorite apps, shortcuts and widgets. In fact, apps that you install on your device, may appear in the Home screen, and in the app drawer, at the same time. Though you can launch an application from either locations, the apps you frequently use should be placed in the Home screen for easier access.

Therefore, it is where you begin to explore your tablet. You can create multiple Home screens, remove a screen, change the order in which they appear, and designate any of the Home screens as the main one. You'll be seeing more about *Home screen organization* in the chapter that comes after this.

Meantime, follow below steps to **add apps to your Home screen**

Your Tab S6 comes preloaded with many Samsung and Google apps. Aside a score of Sammy native apps, you've also got a loaded Google folder containing its trademark apps like *Chrome, Duo, Drive, Gmail, Google search, Maps, Photos, Play Movies & TV*, and *YouTube.*

Yet, you can bet you'll need many more apps to optimize your user experience of the device. And you'll download them mostly from Google Play Store or from Galaxy Store. To get the app you need,

1. From **Home screen**, open **Google Play store**

2. Enter a word or phrase in the **Search bar**. As you do, matching apps and settings list will appear

3. Tap the app you need, then choose from the list of options coming up on your screen

4. Tap **Install** to get the app.

Downloaded app will appear in your Apps list in default. You'll see all apps list by swiping up from the center of your Home screen.

How to customize Navigation buttons

As stated earlier, we'll be talking more about Home screen organization down the line. We return to navigation.

Galaxy Tab S6 Navigation bar, found at the lower part of your screen, bears three buttons, listed below (from left to right):

- Recent apps
- Home
- Back

But you can reorder the navigation buttons, placing the Home key first from left, for instance, or letting **Recent apps** button come last, at the right-hand end.

1. Swipe up from center of Home screen to display all apps

2. Tap to open **Settings** menu

3. Tap **Display** > **Navigation bar**

4. Under Button order, tap an option for any of the arrangements that appeals to you.

Henceforth, your Navigation keys will display in the order you prefer.

How to use Navigation gestures in Galaxy Tab S6

To free up space on your screen, you can the hide the Navigation bar and its keys. You then use gestures to navigate your Tab S6.

To set up gesture navigations,

1. From the Settings page, **tap Display**

2. Touch Navigation bar and select **Full screen gestures**

- Touch **Gesture hints** to show lines at the lower part of your screen where gestures will occur for *Recent apps, Home & Back*

- Touch **Block gestures** with S Pen to stop stylus from performing full screen gestures

You can use hand gestures to navigate your Tab S6. But you can quickly switch between gesture and button navigation by using your *Quick settings* menu

Other Navigation actions on your Galaxy Tab S6

As you explore your Galaxy Tab S6, you'll be doing lots of tapping, swiping, dragging & dropping, as well as pinching in and out of the screen.

> **Light tap**

There's much you can do with just a light tap, and touch and hold actions.

- Tap any item lightly to open it

- You can also tap to select or highlight an item

- Double-tap an image, if you want to zoom it in or out (shrink or enlarge it)

- Tap and hold a Home screen to customize it

- Touch and hold a field to unveil a pop-up menu options

> **The Swipe**

Slide your finger across the screen, or up and down to perform any of the following actions:

- Unlock your device

- Display Home screen apps or menu options

> **Drag & drop**

One way to organize your Home screen items is to touch, hold and move them to new positions.

- Tap, hold and drag app shortcut to add it to a Home screen

- To place a widget in new location, also tap, hold and drag it there.

> **Zoom in/out**

You can magnify or shrink an item on your screen by pinching it with your fingers.

- Push your thumb and forefinger apart on a screen to enlarge an item

- Pinch both fingers together to shrink the item

71

CHAPTER FIVE

HOW TO MANAGE SAMSUNG ACCOUNT IN GALAXY TAB S6 / S6 LITE

You need to sign in to your Samsung account during the setup stage. It's true you can complete the process with a Google account, but that does not diminish the value of adding your Sammy ID in your new Tab S6.

> **Benefits of having Samsung Account in your device**

Sure, there are multiple benefits:

- Helps you keep Samsung apps synced in all your Sammy devices

- Grants you access to Samsung Pay for online purchases

- Helps you get current news and discounts as they become available

- Enables you to use *Find My feature* to track or recover your device if lost or misplaced

- Your Samsung account can be your main webmail.

If you've got an account already, add it to your Galaxy Tab S6 right away.

How to add your Samsung account

1. Swipe up from the center of your Home screen to display all apps

2. Go to **Settings**

3. Select **Cloud and Accounts**, if available, otherwise, tap **Accounts and backup**

4. Tap **Accounts**

5. Touch **Add Account**

6. Choose **Samsung Account.**

In summary, you navigate **Settings** > **Cloud and Accounts** or **Accounts and backup** > **Accounts** > **Add Accounts**, then **Samsung Account**

How to create Samsung Account in your Tab S6

If you didn't have an account before, you can easily create one in your Galaxy Tab S6. Account creation is simple because, your Galaxy device is preloaded with Samsung account software in the settings app.

1. Open the **Settings** app on your Tab S6 screen

2. Touch **Accounts and backup**

3. Tap **Accounts** > **Add accounts** > **Samsung account**

4. Now, you've got options to **Sign in** (if you already have an account) or **Create account** to get one

5. You'll be asked to review and **Agree** some legal information (not sure anyone ever reads them). Like me, just Agree the terms (has anyone ever rejected them) and continue

6. Enter your personal information (user name, phone number, password, and more), then tap **Create account**.

How to remove Samsung Account from your device

In case you want to remove Samsung account from your Tab S6, for whatever reason, it's easy to do so.

1. From the center of your Home screen, swipe up to display all apps

2. Open the **Settings** app

3. Touch **Accounts and backup**

4. Tap **Accounts** and select your **Samsung Account**

5. Tap **Personal info** or **More options,** as applicable to your device

6. Touch Sign out.

Removing an account is a temporary measure. It does not permanently delete the account from your device. But you can also delete an account completely, if you want.

How to delete your Samsung account from Tab S6

This is an extreme measure because it'll delete your entire Samsung purchase history, your content subscriptions, uploads, and profile information. If you want to delete your accounts,

1. Open **Samsung Account** webpage in a browser

2. Enter your **ID** and **password**. Then select **My Account info**

3. Tap the Profile card and open Samsung Account settings

4. Tap **Delete account**, then follow on-screen guide to complete deleting account.

If you have outstanding payment issues, your Samsung Account may not delete. You'll need official Samsung Support to be able to complete the process.

How to find your Samsung ID

It happens to many people in the digital world. You just can't remember the ID to your online space. If it happens to be your ID to Samsung account that you forgot, don't worry. There's a way out.

1. Go to Samsung website and open the **account retrieval page**
2. Enter your information, like user name, phone number, then select **Find My ID**

3. Your Samsung account ID will be displayed.

Hit **Contact Us** for more support, if you still can't recover your ID with the resources available on the account retrieval page.

CHAPTER SIX

LOCKS, FACE RECOGNITION AND FINGERPRINTS FOR DATA PROTECTION

Your Galaxy Tab S6 offers all screen lock types from which you can choose the more convenient way to unlock your device. You've got the usual pattern, PIN and password options. Two biometric lock options, namely Fingerprint and Face recognition, are also available.

To setup a screen lock,

1. Swipe up or down from center of Tab S6 screen to display all apps

2. Open the **Settings** app

3. Scroll to **Lock screen** and tap **Screen lock type**. If asked, enter your current password/PIN/pattern to continue

4. Tap any lock type from the options: **Swipe**, **PIN**, **Pattern**, **Password** or **None.**

If you'll like to set up any of two biometric lock types, *Face recognition or Fingerprint*, you can do so. They sure make for easier access to your device, aside offering protection for your personal information, and authentication for online transactions.

How to setup Face recognition lock type

1. From the center of your Home screen, swipe up or down to display all apps

2. Open the **Settings** app

3. Touch **Biometrics and security**.

4. Then select **Face recognition**. You'll be required to enter a password, PIN or pattern to continue.

5. Read the information and tap **Continue**

At this point, you'll need to follow on-screen guide to register your face, using sensors in your device. It's a simple process lasting no more than a couple of minutes, depending on your confidence.

- Look into the front camera and try to make your face fit in the space marked **Show Your Face**
- Ensure your face fits into **Put your face here** spot
- When your face is captured, you'll see a checkmark in the "Put your face here" screen.

Then, you'll be required to choose a backup method, an alternative way of accessing your tablet if the face recognition fails to unlock it. You can choose either a Pattern or a PIN unlock as backup to face recognition. To do so (in case of Pattern unlock),

- Slide your finger to connect 4 or more dots in any pattern you want

- Repeat the pattern to confirm it

If you want to set PIN unlock as backup to face recognition,

- Enter 4-digit numeric PIN

- Re-enter the numbers to confirm PIN

At this point, your Face recognition unlock is fully set up. And it's easy to use. Once you turn on your Galaxy Tab S6, and look at the Selfie camera in the same way as you did when setting up face unlock, your tablet will open.

How to set up Fingerprint lock in your Galaxy Tab S6

Your Galaxy Tab S6 comes with a vastly improved fingerprint reader, which makes it a secure and very convenient way to protect and access private data on the device.

To set up the feature, or add more fingerprints afterward, these are the steps to follow:

1. Open the **Settings** app by swiping up or down at the middle of your screen

2. Under Personal tab, touch **Lock screen and security**

3. Select **Fingerprints**. A prior screen lock is required to use Fingerprint unlock. So, you'll be asked to enter a password, PIN or pattern to continue this setup. Do so, and tap **Continue**.

4. Follow the on-screen guideline to register your finger.

If you're registering for the first time, you'll be prompted to scan a fingerprint. But if you already have a fingerprint scanned, and want to add another, touch **+Add fingerprint**

It's simple to register a fingerprint, whether in the first instance, or you're adding another fingerprint. But it could be frustrating as well.

For best result, your finger must be clean, free of moisture, oil, lotion, dyes, dirt, any impediment at all.

- When prompted, place your finger on the Home button on the Navigation bar at the lower part of your screen
- Remove the finger when you feel a vibration of the device
- Keep on placing and lifting a finger until percentage reaches 100. The screen will turn green

You need to move your finger around a little on the Home button, even adjust the angle at which you place a finger, each time. The goal is to cover as much of the Home button as possible, otherwise, the system will keep reminding you to do it properly.

You can register four different fingerprints on the device, either all yours, or including your mate's, or anyone else you permit to use your Tab.

How to enter a backup password for Fingerprint unlock

As you did in Face recognition, you also have to set up a password to bail you out when your fingerprint fails to unlock your Sammy tablet.

- Enter 6-digit password

- The password should contain letters and numbers in any combination

- Re-enter the password to confirm it.

With a fingerprint unlock, your device opens in split a second when you place a finger on the Home button. You also need fingerprint authentication to complete a Samsung Pay online transaction.

How to remove a fingerprint from Tab S6

Let's say you added Fingerprint unlock for your mate when the going was good. Now, there's a quarrel and you no longer want them to have access to your Tab S6. No problem, you can easily remove it.

1. Swipe up from the center of Home screen to display all apps

2. Tap the **Settings** icon (a cogwheel) to open the page

3. Scroll to **Biometrics and security**

4. Touch **Fingerprints.** Enter your current password/PIN/pattern, if asked to do so

5. Tap and hold the fingerprint you want to remove, then touch **Remove** at the bottom of view.

To confirm the fingerprint has been removed, review the disclaimer and tap **Remove**

CHAPTER SEVEN

ORGANIZING YOUR HOME SCREEN IN GALAXY TAB S6 / S6 LITE

You've got many options to change the appearance of your Home screen, and make it look just the way you want. To customize Home screen settings,

1. Tap and hold any Home screen

2. Tap **Home screen settings**, then adjust the following areas,

   - **Layout**: You can choose to locate your apps on Home screen, or keep apps screen separate from your Home screen.

- **Home screen app grid**: if you've apps on your Home screen, customize how apps are arranged on the screen. If you created a distinct app screen, you've got to also choose how app icons appear on the Apps screen.

- **Lock Home screen layout**: Enable the lock to prevent anyone removing your apps intentionally, or you doing so by mistake. At the same time, the lock holds your restless apps in check, so they don't jingle out of positions at will. Can be so annoying to see them disorganized, just after you thought you've arranged them neatly!

- **Add apps to Home screen**: By choosing this option, every app you download from Samsung Store or Google Play store will automatically show up on your Home screen.

- **Swipe down to access Notification panel**: When you enable this option, you can open and view notifications by swiping down from any part of your Home screen.

- **Hide apps**: You can hide some apps that you use, for reasons best known to you. They could be adult apps you wouldn't like your kids to access. Or you can hide some apps to reduce the clutter on your Home screen. Choose the apps you wish to hide, and return to the same screen to unhide them when you want. When hidden, the apps can still show in the **Finder** searches since they'.re still installed in your device

- **App icon badges**: When you enable this feature, apps with active notifications will display a badge. You can customize the look of a badge.

When you take the time to organize your device's *Home screen* well, it's easier to find what you need, when you need it. And you're able to predict what your device will do in any situation. So, you optimize your user interface.

How to customize Tab S6 Status bar

The Status bar gives you a quick access to device information (at top-right of Home screen), and Notification alerts, by the left side. Simply pull down the bar from the left, and tap any of the features (Airplane mode, Bluetooth, Wi-Fi availability, Location active, Mute, Vibration, and more) to enable, or disable them.

To configure more changes in the Status bar,

1. In **Quick settings**, tap the 3-dot vertical icon for **More options**

2. Select **Status bar**

- **Tap Show notification icons** to customize how notification alert icons will display on the status bar.

- **Touch Show battery percentage** so you can see the exact battery level displayed in percentage next to the battery icon in Status bar.

Adjusting your Quick setting page

As you already know, you can gain quick access to full device's Settings menu through Quick settings in the Notification panel.

1. Pull down the **Status bar** to open Notification panel

2. Drag it down again to **view all**

- Tap any app in the quick setting to switch it **on** or **off**. For example, the Airplane mode is off by default. Touch it, to switch it on. It disconnects all wireless connection to your Tablet, including voice calls, texts and data.

- Tap and hold a quick setting icon to open its setting

- Touch the **Power** icon to power off, restart or enter Emergency Mode

- Tap **Settings** (cogwheel) icon to quickly get to full device's setting menu.

You can change the positions of Quick setting icons, or reorder the button layout. To do so, tap the *3-dot vertical* icon for **More** options. When you're down customizing your Quick setting view, pull *View all* upward to close it.

CHAPTER EIGHT

15 SETTINGS TO EXTEND YOUR TAB S6 USER EXPERIENCE

How to adjust your Tab S6 Display settings

You've got many options to alter the look and feel of your display. To adjust brightness,

1. Swipe up from center of your **Home screen** to get to your apps

2. Touch **Settings** and select **Display**

3. Tap and hold the blue dot in brightness section, and slide it left or right to decrease or increase screen brightness

4. Touch **Screen mode** and do any of the following,

- Tap to choose vivid or natural color

- Use the slide to cooler or warmer feel

- Switch on or off **Adapative brightness**

At the end of a successful tweaking, your screen will look and feel the way you want.

Setting up secure folder from device settings

A secure folder makes use of native Samsung security platform to create additional protection for apps and data in a folder. To create a secure folder,

1. From the **Home screen**, swipe up from the center to display all apps

2. Touch Settings and select **Lock screen** (or Biometrics) **and security**

3. Touch **Secure folder**

4. Tap **Start**, then sign in with your **Samsung accoun**t when asked to do so

5. Choose your Lock type (PIN, pattern, password or fingerprint) and tap **Next**

When a secure folder has been fully set up, the icon will show up on your screen. You can store personal data in there and nobody is able to access them, even if your device is left unlocked. To open the folder tap the icon and enter the pass code.

How to enable Do Not Disturb in Tab S6

DND mode comes handy when you don't want anyone or any app to interrupt you in the middle of a meeting, bedtime or period of healthful calmness. To set up the mode,

1. wipe up from center of **Home screen** to access your apps

2. Touch **Notifications** > **Do not disturb**

3. Select **Turn on** and choose an option of the period you'll like the device to stay quiet.

It will stay quiet during the period you schedule. Neither calls nor texts and alerts will come announced, except Emergency calls and those you may choose to allow. After the scheduled time, the mode will turn off automatically.

How to Add/Remove Edge panel in Tab S6

Tab S6 comes preloaded with a bunch of apps, including Samsung natives, Google trademarks, even some Windows and carrier apps. Not forgetting the many more you're bound to install from Google play store or Samsung Store.

It's usually a hell lot of work to find your favorite apps from the clutter on the apps tray. Edge panels can make life easy in this regard. And you can add up to 10 edge panels to help locate apps easily.

1. You can edit edge panels and download some other ones, may be, for a fee. Swipe to the left on the Edge panel handle to display a menu

2. Tap the **Settings** icon (looks like a cog wheel)

3. In the listing, touch to select or deselect the edge panels you like to add or remove

---

How to perform factory reset on Tab S6

We customize too many things in our smart devices. It gets to a point when you feel it's better to return your device to factory settings.

Resetting to factory defaults will permanently wipe out everything (yes, everything) you've entered into your device, including, but not limited to Google accounts, Samsung accounts, apps and their settings, stored photos, music collections, and all.

So, before you dabble into factory resetting, ensure to back up everything you won't like lose permanently. Also log into your Google account with current details, and remove **Factory Reset Protection** (FRP) activated automatically during the setup stage of your device.

To perform factory reset,

1. Swipe up from center of your **Home screen** to display all apps

2. Tap **Settings**, then select General **management**

3. Touch **Reset** > **Factory reset**

4. Select **Reset** again, and follow on-screen direction to perform the action.

The device will restart after returning to factory defaults.

How to create scheduled messages in your Galaxy Tab S6

With message scheduling, you can create texts and set a future date or time for it to be delivered.

1. Tap the **Messages** icon to create your text message, as you normally do

2. Enter your message using on-screen keyboard, or the separately sold external keyboard

3. Tap the **More** icon or a **+** sign

4. Select, then touch **Schedule message**

5. Choose a date from the calendar that shows up

6. Set the time you want the message to be sent, and tap **Done.**

At the scheduled time, your message will be delivered automatically. You can attach photo or a video to text messages, whether you're sending instantly, or scheduling them for future delivery.

How to manage app notifications in Galaxy Tab S6

Notifications are useful in alerting you of messages, app information and communications you may need to respond to immediately. But they can irritate with their frequency and sounds.

You've got tools to mute notifications, choose their sounds and volume, set unique sound for each app, choose alert types and determine how notifications behave in your device.

To manage notifications from apps and features,

1. Swipe up from Home screen to access all apps

2. Tap **Settings**, and **choose Notifications**. Customize any or all of the following:

- **Do not disturb**: Block all sounds and notifications as long as this mode is enabled.

- **Status bar**: Choose the number of notification icons that can show on the Status bar.

- **Block specific app**: Turn on or off a toggle next to an app, to block notifications from that particular app. Touch **See all** to view all the apps and choose which ones can show notifications.

• **App icon badges**: Choose apps that can show badges when they get notifications. Choose also whether the badges should display the number of unread notifications.

At any time, you can customize notifications for any particular app, especially those notorious for endless alerts, like most social media apps. To customize notifications for any app,

1. Go to **Settings**. Touch **Notification** and select **See all**

2. Touch an app and customize these options:

- Show notification, so this particular will receive notifications

- App icon badges: If you set an to receive notifications, choose if it should display a badge, and number of notifications

- **Categories**: Tap this option to set notification choices like sound, volume and alert type specific to this app.

By all means, you'll do well to learn all you can about app alerts, so you can manage them well, and prevent them from causing unwelcome distraction at wrong moments.

EPILOGUE

We've taken time and effort to compile Galaxy Tab S6 user guide. It's not all there's to know about this all-purpose device. But we've captured much of what you need to know for you to become duly acquainted with this Samsung's Android tablet, if you already own it.

If you don't own Tab S6, yet found time and energy to pore through the manual, it means you're very interested in it, and will likely get one at the right time.

As you do, remember to use smart devices responsibly. They can be good servants, when properly deployed. But they can become cruel masters when allowed to control our lives.

Smart devices addiction is already recognized as a global problem. Wisdom demands we do all we can to protect our eyes, necks, health and family interactions from being destroyed by an addiction to any tech device or theirs features.

Thanks for patronizing us.

About the Author

MARY HAMILTON is the CEO of *TechVerse,* a renowned software developing organization formed by tech gurus from around the world.

She is also a tech and gadget reviewer, who has written numerous "how-to" manuals for users to get to know their devices better.

Top magazines and tech websites have referenced most of her books as the gold standard for "User guides."

Enjoying her life in a small town in Texas, where she lives with her only daughter, Mary continues to write best-seller books to help improve the tech world.